Chickadee

joy, truth,
cheerfulness

SUE COCCIA

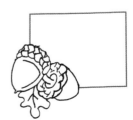

Osprey guardian, creativity, vision

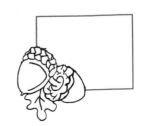

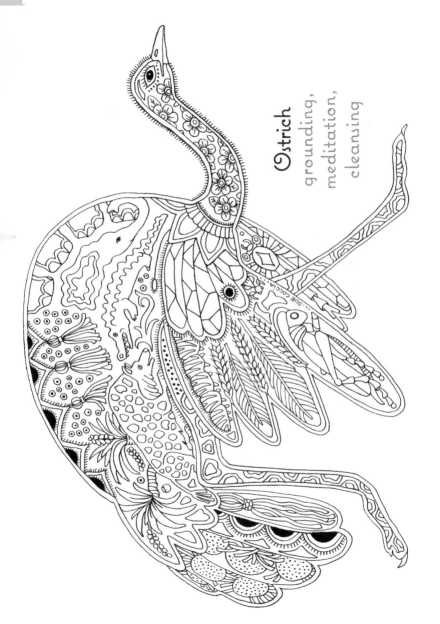

Ostrich

grounding,
meditation,
cleansing

SUE COCCIA

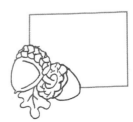

Kingfisher
abundance,
success,
new ventures

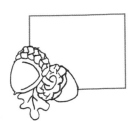

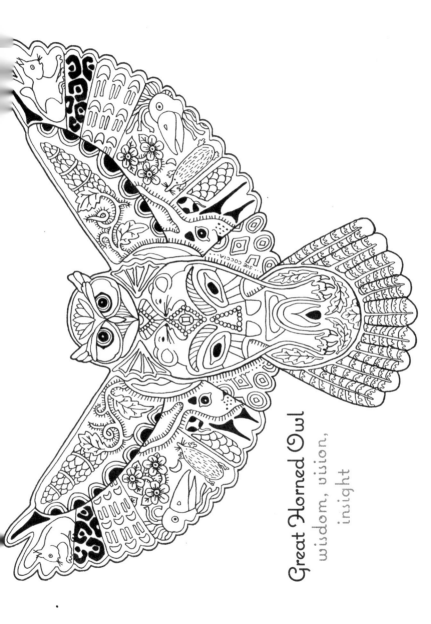

Great Horned Owl

wisdom, vision,
insight

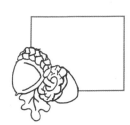

Pelican generosity, resilience, open heart

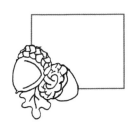

Andean Condor
purification, vision, rebirth

~~~~~~~~~~~~~~~~~~~~~~~~~~~~~~~~~~~~~

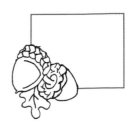

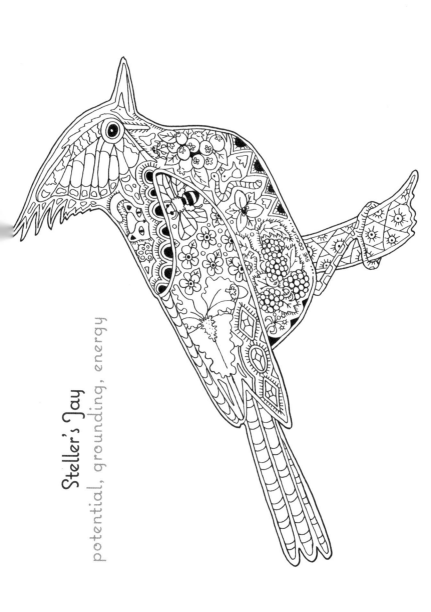

Steller's Jay
potential, grounding, energy

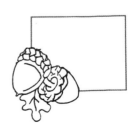

Bald Eagle

connection to spirit,
healing, illumination

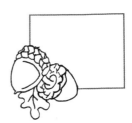

Canada Goose
love of home,
affection, intuition

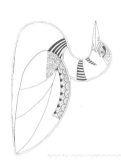

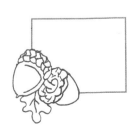

Wood Duck water energy, protection, new opportunities

...SUE COCCIA...

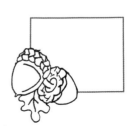

Falcon

power, awareness, success

SUE COCCIA

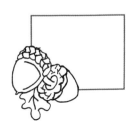

Monarch Butterfly
beauty, joy, soulfulness

Blue Morpho Butterfly *freedom of spirit, balance, grace*

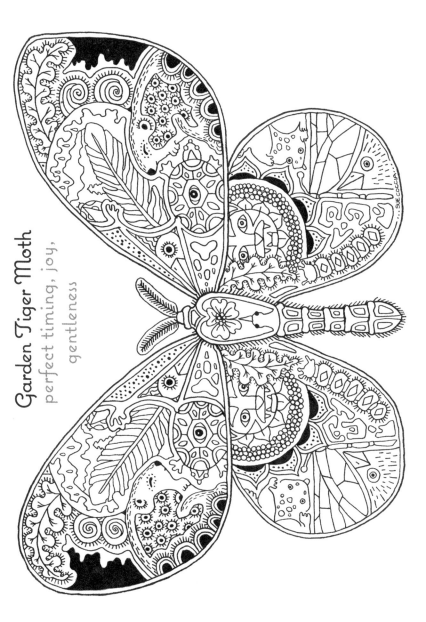

Garden Tiger Moth
perfect timing, joy,
gentleness

Sphinx Moth courage, perception, intuition

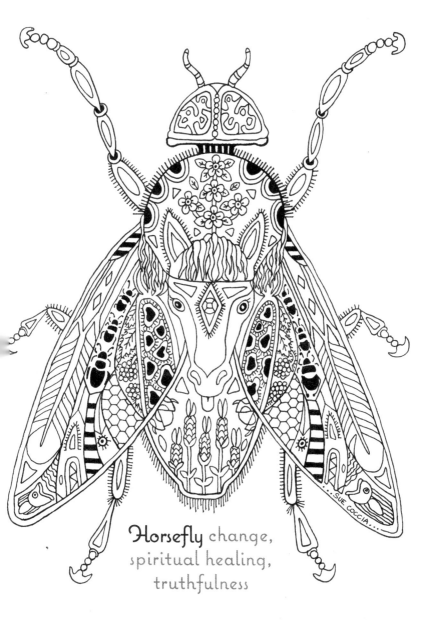

Horsefly change,
spiritual healing,
truthfulness